the
MONKEY
the MOON
& MAYBE

Published and distributed by Front Wheel Learning, a division of Barbara Burke & Associates, Inc. Books and related products may be ordered online via www.MonkeyMoonMaybe.com. Email: bb@BarbaraBurke.com / Phone (507) 663-7232 / Mail: 509 3rd Street East, Northfield, MN USA 55057.

Special discounts are available for quantity purchases by corporations, associations, and book clubs. Special editions, including personalized covers, can be created in large quantities for organizations. For ordering information, call (507) 663-7232 or email SpecialSales@barbaraburke.com.

Cover Design: Carla Brown
Editing and Book Design: Nancy J. Ashmore
Author Photos: Copyright © 2014 by Tom Roster

The Monkey, the Moon & Maybe:
How to Embrace Change and Live Fearlessly

Author: Barbara Burke
ISBN: 978-09907-266-0-9

BUSINESS/SELF HELP
Printed in the United States of America
First printing August 2014

How to Embrace Change & Live Fearlessly

the
MONKEY
the MOON
& MAYBE

Barbara Burke

Author of *The Napkin, the Melon & the Monkey*

Life is about change.
The moon teaches me I can
when I cannot.
— Edie Lazenby

DEDICATION

This book is dedicated to my fellow travelers. May you be happy. May you be healthy. May you be safe. May you live your life fearlessly.

TABLE OF CONTENTS

PROLOGUE

As if on cue, Isabel, the woman with a story for every occasion, delivered another gem. "Olivia, I have a story that may help you see your situation more clearly. It's one of my favorites," she said softly.

"Trapping and selling wild monkeys was a lucrative business in Mexico at one time. Poachers would capture them by placing containers in the forest with a piece of sweet coconut meat inside. The container had a hole barely large enough for the monkey to put its hand in and grab the coconut. But if the monkey tried to withdraw its hand, it found that as long as it kept a grip on the food it was trapped.

What it didn't realize was if it let go of what it wanted, it would go free."

My wise friend looked at me expectantly.

"I get it," I responded, laughing. "It sounds like those monkeys and I have a lot in common! The more obsessed I am with getting promoted to supervisor the more trapped I feel. I keep telling myself that life will be better once I get a new job. But down deep I know that life won't be significantly better. It will just be different, that's all. I'm driving myself crazy worrying about something I have no control over. I did the best I could in the interviews. I need to be patient and wait for HR to make their decision. Like that trapped monkey, I'm creating my own agony by clutching so desperately to what I want. It's time to let it go."

"Indeed," Isabel replied. "You will see that the less attached you are to the outcome, the more powerful you will feel. I guarantee that when you focus less on what may or may not happen in the future and more on remaining in the here and now, you will be much happier."

CHAPTER ONE: THE MERGER

When the boss didn't show up to make his usual rounds I got suspicious. Once or twice a month, our CEO, Mr. Mathwig, would descend from his office on the fifth floor to visit the customer service call center. Coffee mug in hand, he would casually stroll down the rows of workstations visiting with the service representatives. While the topics of conversation varied, he never talked with them about business. He'd ask how their kids were doing in school, check on the score of last night's high school hockey game, or talk about their plans for the weekend. The boss knew the name of every person, their spouse or partner, and their children. The eighty-five service reps that worked in the call center looked forward to their regular chairside chats with Mr. Mathwig. They genuinely liked and cared about the man.

It wasn't always that way. Eight years ago when Mr. Mathwig took over Mighty Power, he was the third CEO in as many years. By the time he arrived the company was in shambles. Eight hundred employees had survived the draconian changes imposed by the last two leaders. We were all afraid he was just another highly paid big talker. But within a few months our new CEO managed to win over even the most skeptical employees.

Mr. Mathwig's popularity was even more remarkable given the fact he made significant— and initially very unpopular—changes during his first year at the helm. While employees balked at being subjected to yet another reorganization, most understood that unless the company got back on track and started making more money, it would, like many small utility companies, go the way of the dinosaur.

Now the word around the office was that our beloved CEO was deathly ill. "Why else would he look so thin?" employees would ask. Besides, all the evidence was there. The man had lost weight and his head was shaved, sure signs he was getting chemotherapy. He was out of the office for a week, supposedly on vacation. But instead of coming back tan and rested, he looked even more worn out. All the evidence added up to Mr. Mathwig having some kind of serious illness. Could be cancer. Might be terminal.

Another rumor that was gaining traction was that the board of directors was about to fire Mr. Mathwig. It was no secret the company was still struggling financially. Even though he had managed to make the company more efficient, he hadn't accomplished what he was hired to do: to return the company to its former glory days.

One Wednesday afternoon every Mighty Power employee received an email from Mindy Hansen, Human Resources manager, informing them of a mandatory all-employee meeting scheduled for 7:30 Friday morning. My boss, Lucy, the Customer Service manager, informed me and the other supervisors that she was holding us personally responsible for getting every service rep on our team to the meeting. There would be no exceptions.

Employees who had been with the company twenty or thirty years could not recall any other CEO calling an all-employee meeting. They assumed that whatever the reason for the meeting, it wasn't to deliver good news. Either Mr. Mathwig was going to announce his departure or, worse, Mighty Power was shutting its doors and everyone would be out of a job.

When the reps on my team asked me what was going on, I could see the fear in their eyes. I told them I didn't know any more than they did. I was as scared as they were.

The only place large enough to accommodate a meeting with all eight hundred employees was the garage at the rear of the building. The cavernous room was filled with row after row of folding chairs. Employees from every department filed in. Very few were joking and laughing. Most sat down quietly in their chairs to wait for the bad news. I had my fingers crossed, hoping I would walk out of the meeting still having a job.

At 7:30 a.m. sharp, Mr. Mathwig strode up to the podium and adjusted the microphone. He looked over the sea of anxious faces, cleared his throat, and said, "Good morning, everyone."

"Thanks for getting up extra early to be here for this historic event. I hope it didn't put too much of a wrench in your morning routine. I realize how unusual it is to have an all-employee meeting like this. I'm sure you are wondering what it's all about.

"I will start by providing an update on Mighty Power's financial performance. Don't worry," he said with a grin. "I promise to keep the number of boring graphs and charts to a minimum. I'll show you just enough to give you an accurate picture of our current situation."

Over the next several minutes our CEO walked the employees through a PowerPoint presentation showing Mighty Power's declining financial performance over the last five years. When he got to the last slide, he paused to give the crowd of silent employees time to absorb the information.

The slide showed an abysmal forecast for the next eighteen months.

"If I were in your shoes, looking at these numbers," Mr. Mathwig continued, "I'd be asking myself why on Earth, with so many new customers, we aren't making more money. If I were you I'd wonder why the latest reorganization and our efforts to cut costs hasn't improved our bottom line. And why, with so many employees taking early retirement, we aren't doing better.

"We are in this situation for a couple of reasons. Being forced to close down the Big Oak nuclear power plant because of its age really hurt us. We manage to produce enough electricity most of the year except during peak periods in the summer and winter months. That's when we have to buy electricity on the open market, at the going rate. Sometimes we actually *lose* money.

"The other reason we are where we are is that even though our expenses are higher, we are not allowed to increase the price customers pay us for electricity. We haven't had a rate increase in twelve years. When we made our case to the Utility

Commission to allow us to raise our rates, they turned us down.

"With profit margins shrinking we needed to find ways to reduce our operating costs. Thanks to all of you, Mighty Power is running much leaner and is more efficient than it was six or seven years ago. When we cut the office supply budget again, Dara in Purchasing asked if I wanted her to start rationing pens and paper clips."

"I told her I didn't think we're at that point yet," he joked.

"I know it's been hard to see so many long-time employees, many of them friends, leave the company to take early retirement. I want you to know how grateful I am to those of you who have stepped up to fill some of the gaps."

"The cold, hard facts, as you saw in the last slide," he said, with a sigh, "are if we keep operating this way Mighty Power will not only fail to make a profit, but lose money this year. Sure, I suppose we could tread water for awhile and hope for a miracle, but that would only put us farther behind. Our loyal shareholders, many of who are in this room today,

Aha! #23

Life is full of surprises.
Expect the unexpected.

deserve a return on their investment. That's only right."

Our CEO went on to explain some of the options he and the board of directors had considered in the last several months. People listened, frowning and murmuring to each other about what it meant. Mr. Mathwig paused a moment to take a deep breath. Looking out at the sea of somber faces, he said, "The other option the board needed to seriously consider was to take up an offer from Imperator Energy, the second largest utility company in the United States, to purchase Mighty Power."

The crowd gasped, then went silent. Billy, one of the senior linemen seated in the back row, jumped up and said, "Wow, Mr. Mathwig. That's not so bad. We thought you were going to announce you had terminal cancer. That you were dying."

The room erupted in nervous laughter.

"Seriously? Is that the rumor going around, that I have cancer?" Mr. Mathwig's eyebrows went up and he rolled his eyes. "Well, I guess I have been looking a bit worn around the edges lately." He ran his hand over his shiny head and chuckled. "Oh, and I suppose when I started shaving my head you all thought I was getting chemo treatments. No, I did that because it was just easier. I'm going bald anyway. The other day my daughter Megan, the one in high school, told me I was looking pretty hip for an old guy.

"Listen, I really appreciate your concern. But I assure you I am not dying of cancer or anything else. I'm just fine.

"I want you to understand"—he raised his voice over our relieved chatter—"that the merger being proposed is not a sure thing. Typically these deals take years to be completed. It will take four or five months for Imperator's people to examine our books and see how we operate. Once they issue their report, Imperator's board will decide if they want to move forward. If they do, we negotiate the terms of the deal. After that, the federal government and state regulators conduct their reviews to make sure the ratepayers are protected and that Imperator Energy's increased size doesn't make it a monopoly.

"Assuming the merger does happen, the

resulting organization will combine the best of both utilities. The new Imperator Energy will have the best plants, the latest technology, and the best people in the industry. I sincerely hope that each of you see this as an opportunity to use your experience, talent, and abilities to help Imperator Energy be not just the best utility company in the nation but the best in the world."

Mr. Mathwig ended his remarks by assuring us he would keep us informed throughout the process and promised to be "as transparent as possible."

I left the meeting relieved to still have a job. What I didn't know was for how long.

THE MONKEY, THE MOON & MAYBE

CHAPTER TWO: KEEPING THE CREW AFLOAT

I felt like the captain of a sinking ship clinging to the hope that I could keep my team afloat until help arrived. It wasn't easy.

It started with the layoffs. Five of the twenty customer service representatives I supervised were temporary employees working under contract. Most had been with Mighty Power for over two years, expecting to eventually be hired as permanent employees. A month after management announced the merger all five temps were terminated.

Team morale tanked. The sudden loss of so many teammates—friends—all at once was devastating. Even my reliable reps, the ones I thought I could count on to show up for work on time, started calling in sick on Mondays, our busiest day, leaving the few who did show up to answer all the calls. Being chronically understaffed made it impossible for us to meet our performance goals. Within a few weeks we had the dubious distinction of being the worst performing team in the call center.

Lenore, my best service representative, remained unfazed. During her years at Mighty Power she had survived three corporate reorganizations and two rounds of downsizing. When I asked how she was doing, she replied in her usual matter-of-fact way, "No biggie. Been there. Done that."

Lorraine recently turned sixty and had been with the company for thirty-four years. Before the merger was announced she never hesitated to tell me exactly what was on her mind. But lately she had very little to say. Being so close to retirement she probably figured the only way she could survive long enough to collect her pension was to keep her head down, work hard, and not do anything to rock the boat.

Ginny, who I privately referred to as "Chicken

Little," had a history of getting worked into a tizzy at the smallest change. So I wasn't surprised when she panicked and did her sky-is-falling routine. Other anxious service reps joined her in the doomsday chorus. Finally I had enough of the whining and called them into my office to deliver some straight talk. I pointed out that they were still receiving a paycheck and the best way for them to continue to be employed was to do what they were hired to do: answer calls and do everything possible to keep our customers happy.

Every morning before the day shift began I gathered my team for a quick huddle. I delivered the same pep talk. After a quick review of the abysmal performance results of the previous day, I let them know how much I appreciated their efforts and thanked them for being there. I emphasized how important it was to get to work on time.

It didn't do much good. Still, too many called in sick. The reps that had unused sick days and personal days figured they'd use them up before they were laid off. I suspected some were already interviewing for jobs outside the company.

Every day was a struggle. Some days we were so short-staffed I had no choice but to ask the reps who did show up to stay late to work mandatory overtime. At first my employees welcomed the time-and-a-half pay they collected for the extra hours they worked. I was proud of how they had adjusted to the situation. In one of our early morning huddles I announced that, depending on how the day went, there was a good chance I would need several of them to stay late to work.

Gretchen had been on my team since she started at Mighty Power two years earlier. She and her husband recently purchased their first house so I assumed she would appreciate the extra income from working overtime. The young woman rarely complained, so when she spoke up I was surprised. "If I have to work late one more time, my husband says he'll file for divorce," she exclaimed. "He's sick and tired of having to rearrange his day so he can pick up Matthew at daycare. I can't blame him. Frankly, I'm sick of it, too. Olivia, when are we going to get some help?"

My team deserved the truth. I gave them part

of it. "Honestly? I have no idea when Mr. Mathwig plans to lift the hiring freeze so I can replace the five people we lost. Look, the only choice we have right now is to make the best of the situation until things get back to normal." What I didn't tell them was that after the merger they would probably look back at today's staffing levels as the good old days.

"Ya, well," said Lanny, a single dad with two teenagers at home and one in college, "I guess we should be grateful to still have a job. Think about it. It could have been a lot worse. If we're smart, we'll just suck it up and deal with it."

Whenever there was a potential downside to any situation, I could count on Nikki to point it out. She and I started at Mighty Power as service reps at about the same time. Folding her arms across her chest, she proclaimed in a loud voice, "You do realize that everybody's saying it's just a matter of time before our call center gets outsourced to some place in Asia. Or that once Imperator Energy buys us they'll close us down and move the operation out of state to their corporate headquarters. Either way, my friends, we are totally and completely screwed!"

Aha! #24

It's not enough to be sorry. Sometimes you actually have to change.

"Hey, as for me? I'm no fool," retorted Brianna, just out of college. "I'm not waiting to see what happens. I'm updating my résumé."

Milo was in his mid-forties and recently divorced, one of the four men on the team. He grinned at Brianna. "Hey, good luck with that. I'm not going anywhere. I'm waiting for that sweet severance package we'll get when the merger is done. I can see it all now, sitting in my boat all day, fishing, drinking beer. Viva la dolce vita!"

All fifteen people started talking at once, their voices getting angrier and louder by the second. I had a mutiny on my hands. How infuriating! Had it occurred to any of them that just maybe this wasn't easy for me either? What was it with these people? We did not have the luxury of spending the rest of the morning talking about their damn feelings! I could hear the echo of ringing phones throughout the center—our customers on hold, waiting for their calls to be answered.

Finally, I had enough. "Okay, okay, I hear what you're all saying! You're worried about losing your jobs. Well, join the club! But, hey! You know what?"

THE MONKEY, THE MOON & MAYBE

I sputtered angrily. "Right now you *have* a job! There are forty calls in queue right now. If you want to remain employed, log in and get to work! And another thing—do it with a smile on your face!"

As I marched back to my office in a huff, red-faced and angry, I regretted what I had said. I don't know who that was back there, but it sure didn't sound like me.

I had just violated two leadership principles I tried to live by every day. Back when I was a service rep, Lucy, our current manager had been my supervisor. The best boss I have ever had. She still has the same sign on the wall in her office. It reads, "Great supervisors do the right thing and follow the Golden Rule." I had let my team and myself down. The last thing they needed was an angry blast from me.

Somehow over the last couple of months, since the merger was announced, I had morphed into a testy, bad-tempered person with a short fuse. I turned into a person I didn't even like. Although I hated to admit it, I had been in the same place earlier in my career.

22 | CHAPTER 2

CHAPTER THREE: DÉJÀ VU ALL OVER AGAIN

When I was hired as a service representative for Mighty Power seven years ago, I thought I had it made. Getting a job with a regular paycheck and paid benefits was important to me, since my husband, Jake, worked seasonal construction jobs and was out of work for months at a time. I figured that a job that involved talking to people on the phone had to be easier than being a waitress on my feet all day trying to earn enough in tips to pay the rent and keep food on the table.

It didn't take long for me to realize how wrong I was! Taking seventy to one hundred calls a day from upset customers blaming me for their problems was a lot more stressful than dealing with an occasional diner complaining that the steak he'd ordered was overcooked. In new hire training I was given some phrases I could use to calm angry customers. But knowing what words to say and remaining calm enough to say them was much harder than it looked.

After about two months on the job, I snapped. It was the worst Monday of my life. The morning started out with Jake and me arguing about money—an almost daily occurrence. Our second-graders Nate and Natalie missed their bus again, so I had to drop them off at school. Had my ancient Honda not taken forever to start, I might have made it to work on time.

When I arrived at the call center the place was in turmoil. Everybody was frantically trying to answer an avalanche of angry calls from customers. No wonder! Some genius in the billing department had messed up and sent thousands of letters to good paying customers. The tersely worded letter said their account was delinquent and if they didn't pay their bill within the next twenty-four hours, their electricity would be shut off.

So many calls hit the call center at once that the phone system crashed. Then the website. Once the phones started working again, hundreds of customers were forced to wait on hold for over an hour listening to the same recorded message over and over again: "Thank you for calling Mighty Power. Your call is very important to us. Please hold for the next available agent." Call after call I was yelled at, sworn at, and called every name in the book. All for a mistake somebody else made.

After being called a "stupid idiot" one too many times, I lost my cool and started fighting back. By the time those next few customers hung up, they probably thought they just had an encounter with the service rep from hell.

I had to get a grip. And fast. If Lucy heard me talk that way to Mighty Power's precious customers I'd be fired for sure. That's when I thought of Isabel, the call center's resident wise woman. She was the senior service rep everyone relied on for answers. When I graduated from new hire training and started taking live calls from customers, she came to my rescue. I needed to be rescued again.

Aha! #25

No matter where you go there you are.

I found my hero in the employee cafeteria standing at the coffee machine. "Oh, hello, Olivia. How are you?" she chirped. I burst into tears. Before I knew it, I was pouring my heart out. I told her about my horrendous day. That I felt like a failure. That more than anything I wanted to be good at this job. But today was proof I would never make it at as a service rep. I was so ashamed of losing my temper with those customers. I feared I was about to get fired. I sobbed even louder as I told her that if I didn't have Jake and the twins I'd get in my wreck of a car and never come back.

Isabel listened without saying a word. Once I finally stopped, she handed me a napkin to dry my tears and said, "Oh, Olivia, I've been where you are." She told me she had a similar experience years ago when she was first starting out. She went to her mother for advice.

"Feeling as though my whole life was caving in," Isabel continued, "I told my mom my sad story. How impossibly difficult my life had become and that my problems were just too much for me to handle. 'I hate my life! You have to tell me what to do!' I pleaded.

"Here is what my mother told me: 'For the ten problems of life that come to us, nothing can be done.' That wasn't what I wanted to hear! "Then is there no way out of this?" I cried. "Am I doomed to be forever screwed up and miserable?

"My mother calmly replied, 'For the ten problems of life—family troubles, work problems and money worries, finding your way in the world—I have no solution. But you have an eleventh problem. For that one I have help.'

"I asked what the eleventh problem was and how it would help me.

"This is what my mother said: 'The eleventh problem is your view that you should not have the ten problems. You can never get away from life's problems. Thinking that you can will always make you want to run from your life.'"

Her mother's advice was spot on. I needed to face reality, too. There is no way around it. I will always have problems. It's crazy to think otherwise.

From that day on, Isabel became one of my

dearest friends. She was a combination life-coach, guardian angel, and the mom I never had. She never told me what I should do to fix a problem. Instead, she told me one of the wisdom stories her mother had told her. These were the same stories parents in her family passed down to their children for several generations. I don't know how many of these stories she has in her collection, but it's almost eerie how she can deliver the perfect story with the exact lesson I need to learn.

THE MONKEY, THE MOON & MAYBE

CHAPTER FOUR:
A NAPKIN, A MELON, AND A MONKEY

Thanks to Isabel I managed to survive those first months as a service rep and eventually found my groove. A year or so later my supervisor, Lucy, was so impressed with my performance she asked me to fill in as a team leader for a few months. I was surprised and very flattered by her offer. Moving up in the company hadn't crossed my mind. I was just happy to have a good-paying job. I didn't think I was ready for that kind of responsibility, so I turned her down. But after considerable prodding from both Lucy and my husband, Jake, I decided to give it a try.

It didn't take long to discover that being a team leader was a lot harder than it looked, especially when the service reps on the team hated each other. With Isabel's help I managed to turn that quarrelsome team around. Later on, when Lucy was promoted to call center manager, she suggested I apply for her old job. After months of tests and countless interviews, I ended up getting the job.

The day I was promoted to supervisor was one of the best days of my life. Once the news got around, a steady stream of co-workers stopped by to congratulate me. As I was gathering my things to leave for the day, I looked up to see Isabel standing at my workstation. She presented me with three beautifully wrapped boxes. I could tell by the look on her face that these were no ordinary gifts.

I opened the smallest box first. It contained an industrial-looking dispenser filled to the brim with napkins. "So I can always remind myself of the idea you drew for me on a napkin," I said with a laugh.

Package number two was large and very

heavy. This one contained a big ripe watermelon, a reminder of the Fighting Melons story Isabel told me that helped me to get my team to work together.

Knowing what was in the first two boxes, I should have guessed what was in the third. Box number three contained a toy monkey to remind me of the story of the trapped monkey.

"A napkin, a melon, and a monkey." I laughed, tears in my eyes. "Thank you, Isabel. I'll treasure them always."

I kept the cheery little monkey on my desk in my new office and named him "Izzy," short for Isabel. His caramel-colored coat was soft and furry. His sparkling amber eyes and crooked half-smile made him look as if he was just about to laugh. Measuring about thirteen inches from head to toe, he sported a long tail with a curl at the end. My Izzy was pretty cute in a monkey sort of way.

Most days I enjoyed my new role as a supervisor. But on those occasions when I felt anxious and stuck and couldn't figure out why, I'd look into Izzy's friendly face and ask myself if the reason I was feeling that way was because I was acting like the trapped monkey in Isabel's story.

Later on, when I moved to a different office I put Isabel's gift up on a bookshelf and forgot about him. My furry friend had been sitting there for years, witnessing my gradual fall from happiness.

Isabel is now happily retired. On those Saturdays when I have to drop one of the kids off for soccer or swimming practice, we meet for coffee. This Saturday I arrived with a problem—the biggest yet.

Once we got our coffee and sat down, I jumped in, telling my wise friend how doomed and depressed I felt, how unmanageable my team had become, and how many signals I was getting that they were turning against me.

"And then there's my job! The thought of losing the best job I'll ever have has me tied up in knots!" I exclaimed.

Isabel smiled, took a sip of her coffee, and said, "Ah, yes. Life certainly can get messy at times. It's been messy before and it will be again. There is no escaping it, Olivia."

"Isabel, you can be so frustrating at times!" I

shot back. "You don't seem to be at all bothered by the fact that my life is about to change forever! I could be out on the street looking for another job tomorrow!"

"That's because I am a realist, Olivia," she shrugged. "The way I see it, there are two kinds of people in this world—realists and strugglers. As a realist I recognize that life is messy. To think that life should be neat, tidy, and predictable is a recipe for unhappiness. Realists look at the highs and lows of life like the weather. One day it can be beautiful and sunny and the next dismal and rainy. Complaining about the weather is a waste of time. Wait long enough and conditions always change. Realists understand that nothing in life is permanent and the only thing we can really count on is change. That's why they aren't surprised when something happens they didn't expect and their circumstances suddenly change. Instead of dwelling on the downside, realists have the confidence of knowing that painful situations don't last forever. Because they go with the flow, realists are happier and less stressed.

"The strugglers, on the other hand, are

Aha! #26

Life is messy.
(It's supposed to be.)

constantly searching for safety and security. They have the mistaken idea that they should be exempt from life's problems and believe the only way they can be happy is if life goes their way. They want their lives to be tidy and predictable, so they waste considerable effort trying to control events (and people) that are outside their control. When strugglers encounter a change they didn't expect and don't like, a change that messes up their carefully crafted plans, they are thrown off track. They complain. They blame. They bewail what could have been. Instead of looking at change as a potential opportunity, strugglers feel victimized. Strugglers live in a perpetual state of dissatisfaction. They believe they will be happy once conditions are just right, telling themselves, things like: 'I'll be happy when I get a bigger house, a new car, the next promotion, or the latest smart phone.' Ironically, the strugglers, the people who are constantly searching for what will make them happy are the least likely to find it."

"Right," I replied, "the strugglers suffer from what your mother called the Eleventh Problem.

They think they shouldn't have the ten problems of life. I know what that feels like. I already learned that lesson the hard way."

"I wonder if you really did learn that lesson," replied Isabel. "Olivia, of the two types of people, realists and strugglers, which would you say you are?"

"Right now, I'm probably more of a struggler than a realist," I admitted. "Even though I know that's what I'm doing, I can't seem to let go of the fear I'm feeling. Honestly? I'm terrified! I don't want my life to change. Isabel, I don't just want to keep my job—I *need* to keep my job! What if I have to start my career all over again? I had a future!"

"And what about the loss of income!" I cried. "Sure, what money I get from the severance package would pay the bills for awhile. But if I don't find another job right away that pays as well, which is pretty likely, Jake and I will be in a real bind. We have no savings to get us through. We used every cent we had to make the down payment on our new house."

"Olivia," she said softly, "I wonder if the situation, the possibility of you being laid off, is the

THE MONKEY, THE MOON & MAYBE

problem. Could it be the real issue here isn't being out of a job? That the real problem is how you are choosing to respond to the possibility? I have to say you have managed to spin an impressive worst-case scenario. A scenario which, I remind you, may not happen."

"Seriously!" I exclaimed. "So you think I'm just making this up? Do you really think that being laid off wouldn't be a problem for me? Then you clearly don't understand the seriousness of the situation!"

Instead of leaving the café feeling better about my predicament, as I had hoped, I felt worse. A hundred times worse.

39 | CHAPTER 4

THE MONKEY, THE MOON & MAYBE

CHAPTER FIVE: THE SPACE IN THE MIDDLE

My friendship with Luis meant the world to me. Years ago when we were team leaders he and I competed for a supervisor job that eventually went to me. Luckily, a few months later there was another opening and he joined me as a supervisor. Luis became my closest friend. No matter how bad or crazy things got, we knew we could count on each other. We had each other's back.

Luis was a big guy with an even bigger heart. At 38 years old he still looked like the football player he had been in college. His sense of humor was legendary. Whenever he caught me obsessing about something, he would make me laugh by singing me a couple of lines of his favorite Bob Marley song, complete with the Jamaican accent: "Don't worry 'bout a thing. 'Cause every little thing gonna be all right!" It worked every time.

When I arrived at my office early one morning I was surprised to see Luis waiting for me. "Good morning. Got a minute?" he asked. He looked worried. I closed the door. I wondered what was wrong.

My friend took a deep breath. "Olivia, I wanted you to be the first to know about the decision Tina and I made last night. I'm finally going to do it," he said excitedly. "I've decided to quit! I've always dreamed of owning my own business. So when Tina's dad asked if we were interested in taking over his dry cleaning business after he retires, we jumped at the chance. The plan is for me to leave after the merger is finalized. I'll take whatever severance package they offer."

I was stunned. I felt as though I'd been punched in the stomach. I couldn't believe my best pal, the supervisor I was closest to, could be leaving. When I realized he wasn't kidding, my eyes filled with tears. "Why didn't you say something? You can't just up and leave me!" I sniffed.

Luis reached over and gave me a hug. "Oh, don't be like that. I didn't want to tell you until I made my final decision. No use getting you all upset before I knew for sure. Olivia, I'm so very sorry. You've been the best friend ever. I'll miss you, too. But please, try to understand. I gotta do what I gotta do."

"It's a great opportunity for you, Luis," I conceded. "I can't blame you for taking it. But that doesn't mean I'm not going to miss you." I turned away to hide my tears and looked around my office. On the top of the bookshelf my eyes fell on my toy monkey, Izzy. I reached way up to get it, gave it a hug, and handed it to my departing friend. A going away present. Obviously touched, Luis took the toy monkey, patted it on the head, and handed it back to me. "Aw, that's very generous of you, Olivia, but you know I already have a monkey identical to this one. Isabel gave it to me when I got my promotion to supervisor."

"Wow! Really?" I slid out my desk drawer and dug around until I found what I was looking for. I held up a folded paper napkin. "Did Isabel give you one of these, too? A napkin with two circles and a space in the middle?"

"She got to you, too?" Luis laughed. "Actually, yes, Isabel gave me a napkin with that same diagram. I had mine framed. It's hanging on the wall of my den at home. It's there to remind me to stop struggling so much, to stop pushing up against what I don't like and have no power to change.

"My big aha! moment came several years ago when the recession hit. Tina was laid off her high-paying management job without any notice. We thought about downsizing and selling the house we recently bought, but there was no way to do it without taking a huge loss. The house had lost that much value practically over night. Between trying to make a mortgage payment we could no longer afford and having three little boys to support on my salary alone, we found ourselves getting further and further behind. It got so bad we were on the verge of filing bankruptcy.

"Olivia, I never felt so sick, so stuck, or so desperate as I did then. I wracked my brain for weeks trying to figure out how I could save my family from financial ruin. I just couldn't see a way out.

"I went to Isabel for advice. She sat me down, took a napkin from the dispenser on the table and drew two circles with a space between them. I remember thinking how crazy it was. There I was hovering over a napkin, being asked to picture myself as the circle on the right bumping up against the circle on the left—my bleak financial situation. Isabel told me it was an illustration of a powerful concept that had been passed down through many generations of her family. I imagined a scene a hundred years ago. Two people standing shoulder to shoulder as one of them sketched out the same picture in the dirt using a stick.

"As Isabel explained the meaning of the diagram, I got it! That was exactly what I was doing—I was spending all my energy pushing up against, trying to impact, a situation I had no power to change. What I needed to do was to be patient—to stop in what Isabel called the 'space in the middle,' the space between the two circles. That, she said, is the location of my personal power.

Isabel told me that if I could stop pushing against what I didn't like, my financial situation—even for a minute or two—I would regain my balance and tap into that inner strength I didn't know I had. She said if I could make that shift in perspective I would see what options I really had.

"That evening as I was driving home I felt energized and more optimistic. After dinner I showed Tina the napkin that Isabel gave me and explained the diagram with two circles and a space in the middle. My wife was as astonished as I was to discover something so simple could illustrate such a profound and liberating concept.

"For the first time in months we were able to discuss our finances without fighting. We agreed to take a hard look at our spending habits, to cut back on extras, sell some stuff we didn't need, and do a better job of budgeting so we could survive on my paycheck. Luckily, Tina landed another good-paying job a few months later. That was a huge relief."

"Luis," I replied, smoothing the napkin, "I had no idea Isabel gave you the same advice she gave me. If she gave you the napkin, she must have introduced you to SODA, too."

"She did!" Luis laughed. "*Stop. Observe. Decide. Act.* The magical four steps that saved me more times than I can count."

"Me, too!" I replied. "When I was a new service rep I was incredibly naive. I was not at all prepared for the steady flow of really angry, upset customers calling me names and blaming me for whatever mess they were in. Even though I was trained to not take it personally and tried not to, once they started yelling at me I would forget and get defensive. But once Isabel told me that the trick to remaining calm was remembering to *Stop* for a millisecond and *Observe* without judging the situation as good or bad, right or wrong, without getting emotional, I would have the power to *Decide* on the best solution and *Act* with confidence."

"It worked!" I exclaimed. "When I started using SODA as Isabel suggested, I was amazed. Customers, even the ones who started out crazy-mad, ended up thanking me for my help and singing

Aha! #27

React or respond.
You decide.

my praises. If I hadn't learned to use SODA, I would not be sitting in this chair today!"

"You know," Luis responded, "I had another revelation when I realized that *Stopping* long enough to see situations clearly, minus the emotion, not only was a lifesaver when it came to dealing with my customers, it helped me be a better parent. Between the three of them, my boys can come up with a million ways to break the rules and get into trouble. But once I started applying SODA, I stopped getting so upset. I stopped yelling at them. I saw the truth—my little guys were kids, not miniature adults. When I started being more relaxed around them, life at our house was a lot less stressful."

"I know what you mean about life getting easier," I replied. "When I first started using SODA in other areas of my life, I discovered the situations that used to upset me, didn't matter anymore. Take driving on the freeway, for example. Some mornings by the time I got to work I'd already be in a foul mood, angry because another driver cut me off or somebody was driving too slow in the fast lane. But when I started looking at these situations with new eyes, it dawned on me that whatever these drivers were doing wasn't intended to make me mad. I did that all on my own."

Luis looked at his watch and exclaimed, "Whoa! I gotta go. I have a meeting in five minutes!" As he gave me a quick hug good-bye, I felt very sad at the prospect of not seeing him every day. But I knew this wasn't about me. Of course, I wanted my good friend to be happy. So, if Luis needed to leave Mighty Power to run his own business I had to support him.

CHAPTER SIX: A GIFT THAT KEEPS ON GIVING

After Luis left, I shut the door and propped Izzy, my happy little monkey, up on my desk. As I looked into his shiny amber eyes, I said, "Well, little buddy. I guess it's just you and me from now on."

I held him close and gazed into his smiling face. My eyes welled up with tears. Holding the monkey even tighter, I sighed and said, "Just when I thought it couldn't get any worse, I find out my best friend is quitting. You know, it hardly seems fair. Up until a couple of months ago, I was going along, happily living my life, feeling pretty content with the way things were going, believing I had a secure future ahead of me and then suddenly my nice little life gets blown apart. What about that is fair?"

The phone rang. It was Isabel calling.

"Hello, Olivia," said Isabel. "I wanted to check in with you, to see how you are doing. Is this a good time? I hope I'm not interrupting anything."

"Oh, nothing important," I sighed. "I was just telling my furry monkey friend here, you know, the one you gave me, how stuck I'm feeling right now. How unfair life is. I find he is an excellent listener."

"So, is he giving you some good advice? I hope he didn't tell you that life is *supposed* to be fair," she chuckled.

"Actually, he's not much of a talker. It's been pretty much a one-sided conversation," I replied. "I suppose you think I'm crazy telling my troubles to a toy monkey."

"Oh, not at all!" replied Isabel. "Actually, when I gave you the monkey, that is precisely what I hoped would happen, that having him around would remind you of the story of the stuck monkey.

"I suspect that if your monkey could talk he'd tell you the same thing I've been trying to get you to understand. That the reason you are feeling so miserable right now is because you can't seem to let go of that precious job of yours."

I glanced over at Izzy sitting on my desk. I thought I saw him look up at me as if to say, "Take it from me, a former stuck monkey, she knows what she's talking about!"

"Olivia, I didn't feel very good about how we left our conversation on Saturday. You were pretty upset when you left. I can certainly appreciate how much you value your job. It's perfectly natural to want to hang on to something so important to you."

"Isabel," I replied. "It's not that what you were telling me didn't register. It did. Intellectually, I *know* I am way too attached to my job. But that's only part of it. What I'm really afraid of is being forced to let go of the life I have now. Until this merger thing happened, I was blissfully cruising along. No big worries. I had it all—a job I loved, a bright future, a loving family, good health, everything anybody could want. I really thought I was all set."

"But what bothers me the most," I continued, "is how stupid I was not to have taken the lessons I learned the first time around more seriously."

Isabel said softly, "Intelligence has nothing to do with it, my dear. Just about everyone at some time in their life experiences what you did a few years go. Their life stops working. The wheels fall off. They become so dissatisfied and unhappy and are in so much pain they do whatever it takes to get their life back on track. Once the changes they make take effect, their life gets better. Easier.

"But here's the trap—they become so comfortable with the way things are, they forget what they learned, the very things that enabled them to get their life back on track. What they fail to realize is that until they make those hard-earned life lessons a permanent part of who they are, they are doomed to experience the same pain and struggle again and again."

"Olivia, it's time to stop blaming yourself," advised Isabel. "Believe me, most people do the same thing you're doing. That is until they figure out that their life would be a whole lot easier if they changed their point of view.

"That's what being truly happy is—a matter of perspective," Isabel continued. "As I said, the happiest people I know expect the unexpected. So when they are hit with something they didn't expect or even want, they don't waste energy feeling like a victim. They go about finding a skillful way to deal with the situation."

"Olivia, my friend, I have confidence in you. Now that you know better, you will do better. Rediscover those lessons from last time. Let go of the fear of what may or may not happen tomorrow and stay right where you are—in the present. I guarantee that once you do you will see your situation for what it is."

Isabel was right. I needed to stop obsessing about what was going to happen after the merger. It was time to stop being such a struggler, trying to make my life perfect. It was time I lived in the real world.

That reminded me of an arcade game I played once, called "Whack-a-Mole." Picture a board with several rows of holes. The object of the game was to use a rubber mallet to whack as many of the moles as possible as they popped up in rapid, random succession. Trouble was, I no sooner hit one mole than five more would pop up and disappear before

I could hit a single one. I remember laughing to myself and thinking that the game of Whack-a-Mole was a lot like life—a series of unplanned and random events, most of which were outside my control.

That evening Jake came home late again from work, made a sandwich, and went straight downstairs to his office. He barely said hello to me. Lately, my husband and I rarely talked. If we had to make arrangements to pick up one of the kids from a game or activity, we would exchange texts or leave a note on the kitchen counter. I wondered if he really was as busy with his construction business as he claimed or if he was avoiding me. I hoped that wasn't the reason why.

After I fed the kids dinner (frozen pizza again), I loaded the dishwasher, helped them with their homework, gave them each a hug, and sent them off to bed. I decided to go for a walk. I had a lot to think about.

It was a crisp autumn evening. A bright orange harvest moon hung low in the sky. As I walked along in the moonlight, the fallen leaves crunching under my feet, I thought back to that painful time seven years ago when I was a new service rep and felt so overwhelmed by what seemed like an endless parade of problems.

The first thing I needed to do now was start to use SODA again. It is a pretty simple idea and not that hard to do. The trick is to remember to do it.

As I walked along, I looked up at the moon, held my hand to my heart, and vowed to be more mindful, to stop long enough to see situations clearly and choose the best response.

The second idea Isabel introduced me to, which also made a huge difference in my life at the time, was taking a few minutes during the day to unplug. Until I met her, I had no idea there was a place in my head I could retreat to, to get away from the craziness of my job and get some peace and quiet. That safe, peaceful refuge had been there my whole life. I just hadn't realized it.

When I first got to know Isabel, I admired her ability to stay so cool and calm. I never saw her get rattled or upset. Her secret, she said, was her daily practice of unplugging. Isabel's instructions sounded easy enough: sit quietly with my hands in my lap

Aha! #28

We all have inner wisdom.
A true friend helps us find it.

and my feet on the floor and focus on counting my out breaths. She warned me it would take some practice to get the hang of it but that once I did, I, too, would feel more calm and confident—and a lot less stressed.

I decided to give unplugging a try. Every day for two weeks during my afternoon break I went to a vacant office upstairs. I did everything Isabel told me to do. But I failed every time. As hard as I tried, I could not stop myself from thinking. I could not figure out what I was doing wrong. When I complained to Isabel about how much trouble I was having, she told me I was making the mistake most beginners make when they start on this path— trying to stop my thoughts.

"That's impossible," she said. "Just as your heart is constantly pumping blood throughout your body, your mind generates a steady flow of thoughts. You could be thinking about what to have for lunch one second and fantasizing about winning the lottery the next. Your mind is devoted to filling itself up with thoughts.

"The idea is to observe your thoughts and feelings as they float in and out. When you notice a thought simply say to yourself, 'That's a thought. Let it go.' Then return your attention to your breath. Noticing you are hooked on a thought is exactly what's *supposed* to happen—notice, let go, come back to the present moment. Repeat.

"Olivia, I urge you to continue spending a few minutes each day unplugging. It will enable you to be more aware, more in touch with life. When you take a step back to see situations clearly, without judging them as good or bad or right or wrong you become more mindful. You will discover what I did, that the more mindful you are, the easier life gets.

"Be patient. You'll get there. There's a reason we call it a 'practice.'"

Isabel was right. The more I practiced, the easier it got. I found that quieting my mind and bringing my thoughts back to that quiet place gave me the mental discipline to apply SODA when I needed to.

As I walked along enjoying the peace of that evening, I looked up at the moon, placed my hand on my heart again, and made a second promise: to take some time every day to unplug. I could close the door to my office and sit quietly or, when the weather was nice, leave the building and sit on a bench in the park across the street. I could take a walk around the block. I promised myself that no matter how busy I was I would take at least ten minutes for myself during the workday.

Unplugging and using SODA reminded me of one of the Aha!s, bits of wise insights I wrote down during my initial transformation. I wrote all 22 Aha!s on post-it notes so I wouldn't forget. Aha! #20 was one of my favorites and certainly applied to my current situation: "It's not what happens to you in life, it's what you do with what happens that counts."

I had to locate those twenty-two Aha!s again. I made my third commitment of the evening— incorporate those hard-earned lessons into my life once again. But first—I needed to find where I put them.

THE MONKEY, THE MOON & MAYBE

CHAPTER SEVEN: PROMISES ARE MADE TO KEEP

When I returned from my walk, I went to find Jake. I found him in his favorite spot—on the couch in the living room watching a game on TV, sipping a beer. I knew how he hated to be interrupted during a game. I touched his shoulder.

"Honey," I ventured.

"What?" he grunted without looking up from the football game.

"Sorry to interrupt, but I have a question. Any idea where those sticky notes with the Aha!s are? They used to be on the fridge in our old house."

"Nope. Haven't seen them since we moved. Try the garage."

A commercial appeared on the screen. My husband turned the volume down and looked at me. "Ah, just curious. Why the sudden interest?" he asked. "I thought you forgot abut those Aha!s of yours. You haven't mentioned them in, what—years?"

"I know. I just need to find them that's all," I replied, a tad defensive.

I glanced at the TV. The commercial had ended. The game was back on. Sure it was the end of our conversation, I headed for the door.

"Wait a minute," he said. "Don't go. We need to talk."

I went back to the couch and sat down next to him.

"If looking for those Aha!s," Jake continued, "means you're thinking about revisiting them, thinking you may want to get back to using them again, I'm glad. I know those little sayings meant a lot to you at one time. We used to joke about them, remember? Like when one of us did something we knew we should apologize for, but were too stubborn to actually say the words, we'd point to Aha! #9 on the fridge to remind ourselves, 'A simple apology works wonders.'"

We both laughed. It had been a long time since we shared a laugh.

"Oh, Jake, you're right. I do need to dust off that Aha! and probably a few others," I confessed.

Before I could say anything else, Jake jumped in. "Now that we're on the subject, there is something I've been meaning to talk to you about." After pausing a moment, he said, "Okay. Well, I guess this is as good of a time as any. I might as well tell you now."

Given the grave look on his face, I knew whatever he had to tell me wasn't anything I wanted to hear.

My husband took my hand in his and looked me in the eye. "It's about your attitude, Olivia. Honey, I've seen you in bad moods before, but I've never seen you like this. When it first started a couple of months ago, I was hoping your short fuse was temporary, that you were going through some tough stuff at work. I kept waiting for you to bounce back, to be your usual optimistic self. But that hasn't happened. In fact, it's gotten so bad—

honestly, sometimes I don't even want to be in the same room with you."

"I know, I know," I said, "but—"

"Olivia, according to you, none of us can do anything right. You get mad at the kids for stuff you used to let pass. Now if they don't hang up their jacket or forget to make their bed, you act as though the world was coming to an end. It's not fair to the kids, or to me, to have to walk around on eggshells afraid of saying or doing anything that could set you off. In fact, I've had it with you being so negative and cranky. You have *got* to get a grip!" he exclaimed loudly.

I was so shocked and so ashamed, I began to cry. My husband put his arm around me, drew me near, and said softly, "Hon, I know you probably don't realize you are bringing all the stress you're feeling at work home with you.

"Really, what I want," he continued, "is for you to go back to being the Olivia I used to know— that happy, go-with-the-flow wife of mine. The one that used to be a pleasure to live with."

"I'm so sorry," I sniffed. "Jake, I love you and the kids so much! I am so sorry for behaving like such an idiot."

"Hey, don't get so down on yourself. I know you. You'll bounce back," he said softly, stroking my cheek. "I think the threat of the merger has shaken your confidence. You're a little off your game right now, that's all. You're like a baseball pitcher who's been on a long winning streak and starts losing games. The only way to get back on top is to not dwell on his losses. What you need to do now is look at every day as your chance to get back in the game. Olivia, you know what it feels like to be happy and take life in your stride. You know what it feels like to be a winner. You've done it before. I know you can do it again."

That's my Jake, a coach at heart.

He gave me a quick kiss and said, "Now, scoot! I've got a game to watch." It felt good to clear the air and reconnect with him. As that Aha! says, an apology really does work wonders.

When I walked out of the room I put my hand

on my heart a fourth time that evening and vowed to be more present for my family. A family I'm so fortunate to have.

I went out to the garage, switched on the light, and looked around until I located the one remaining box from the move labeled KITCHEN. I got it down, opened the box and right on top was an envelope containing the lost notes. My precious little yellow squares of wisdom.

The next morning as I drove to work I went over the promises I'd made to myself the previous evening—what I needed to do to get back in the game, as Jake put it. I promised to take ten minutes a day to unplug, to slow down and apply SODA when I needed to, and to start living the twenty-two Aha!s I accumulated years ago. But the fourth promise I made to myself was the most important of all: to stop being so self-obsessed and start showing up for my family.

When I got to my office, I pinned all twenty-two yellow notes [see Page 124] on the bulletin board next to my desk. I took care of the pile of emails in my in-box and returned a couple of phone calls. Just before I left for my first meeting, I picked up my cheery monkey friend and gave him a squeeze. "Well, Izzy, this is it, the moment of truth. Let's see if I can live up to those lofty promises of mine."

The first meeting was with Curtis, Mighty Power's credit manager. I wanted to lobby for a thirty-day credit extension for a long-time customer, a single mom I helped a few years ago. Now she was in a similar situation. Having been laid off for several months, she was behind on her bill. Once she got the first paycheck from her new job, she'd pay the entire amount. I knew she was good for it. I made what I thought was a convincing case on her behalf. But Curtis turned me down flat, citing the company's "dire financial situation" as the reason.

Before this I would have argued with him and, having lost, be in a grouchy mood the rest of the day. But this time, I applied SODA. I stopped long enough to see the situation for what it was. As credit manager he had the final word. Like it or not, I had to accept his decision.

Aha! #29

Sometimes learning is remembering what you already know.

After that meeting, I met with the "Fun Committee," the group of service reps tasked with coming up with at least three ideas for fun activities that would improve employee morale. Feeling demoralized themselves, they told me they were sorry, but they couldn't come up with a single fun idea. Instead of showing my frustration, I applied SODA a second time. I gave them a pep talk and told them how confident I was in their creative abilities and urged them to try again. It must have worked. The Fun Committee breezed out of the meeting excited about their assignment.

The morning was topped off by settling an argument between three long-time employees who wanted to take the day after Thanksgiving as a vacation day. Normally these people got along fine. But when it came to getting the vacation days they wanted, there was no room for compromise. Instead of getting frustrated and making an arbitrary decision, I decided to use a different approach. The question was settled with a couple rounds of Rock Paper Scissors.

The morning had flown by. I felt proud of the way I'd handled the challenges thus far. Stepping back to calmly consider the best way to handle these situations, to stay in the space in the middle, without getting upset, had really paid off. I actually felt calm for a change.

At noon I decided to act on my promise to unplug for a few minutes each day. Instead of going to the cafeteria for lunch as usual, I remained in my office. I shut the door, placed Izzy on my lap, and settled into my chair. Recalling Isabel's instructions, I sat up straight with my feet on the floor, closed my eyes, and took a long, deep breath.

> "Okay ... let's see if I remember how to do this. ... Focus on my breath ... Breathe in ... Slowly ... breathe out ... That's right ... breathe in ... breathe out ... Slowly ... That's it ... ah, that's it ... Breathe in ... breathe out ... We're out of milk and peanut butter, I'll have to stop at the grocery store on the way home. I wonder if I took the grocery list with me. It was on the kitchen counter with my keys. ... Oops, that's a thought ... thinking ... Okay ... Let it

go … Come back … Breathe in … breathe out … breathe in … breathe out … breathe in … breathe out … That's it … Breathe in … breathe out … Slowly … breathe in … breathe out … breathe in … I sure hope this works. … I've got to get a grip … I'll have to make it up to the kids for being such a grouch … when I got like this before, they were little and I'd hear them whisper behind my back "Oh, oh! Mommy's got her crabby pants on again." Oops … that's a thought … let it go … back to the breath … feet are on the floor … That's a thought … Breathe in … breathe out … breathe in … breathe out … I am feeling more relaxed … Ahh … That's a thought … Let it go … Breathe in … breathe in … breathe out … Mmmm, what time is it? … "

I opened my eyes and was surprised to see the clock said 12:30 p.m. A half hour had flown by—not just ten minutes. I looked down at my lap and whispered to Izzy, "Hey, little buddy, maybe there is hope for me yet!"

CHAPTER EIGHT: A TEAM OF STUCK MONKEYS

Every employee at Mighty Power received the same notice from the Human Resources department about the mandatory interviews. The email said that as part of preparing for the merger with Imperator Energy, all Mighty Power employees were required to reapply for the jobs they currently occupied. It went on to say that if an employee chose not to complete the job application and the personal interview by the deadline, they could be terminated.

The day before the email was sent, Mindy, the HR manager, called a meeting of the supervisors and managers to prepare us for the inevitable fallout.

"Having been through a couple of mergers

THE MONKEY, THE MOON & MAYBE

myself," she began, "I know from experience when employees receive the mandatory reapplication notice, they will be nervous about their future with the company."

That was an understatement.

"Clearly, it's a difficult situation for you to be in. As members of Mighty Power's management team you are probably concerned about your own jobs. I understand that. But I'm asking you to put your personal feelings aside, so we can present a united front. I want one hundred percent of your employees to go online, set up their interviews, and complete the employment application by next Friday. No exceptions."

Having been forewarned, I wasn't surprised the next morning when I found my entire team crowded into the conference room next to my office waiting for me. I stopped by my office to retrieve my pal Izzy from my desk. I had a feeling I'd need all the help I could get.

"They can't be serious!" protested Lanny, waving a copy of the email. "I've been doing this job for four years and they want me to apply for it all over again? What do they think, that I've been doing a lousy job all this time? This is absolute crap!"

Nikki was next. "It figures! Here we go! These interviews are a just a sneaky way to get whatever documentation they need so they can fire us."

"Sure," said Gretchen, on the verge of tears, "they say they'll give us a choice of whatever jobs are left after the merger. They'll give us a choice all right! If we do manage to pass the interview—and that's a big 'if,'—they'll either kick us to the curb or tell us we are welcome to uproot our families and move a thousand miles away to work in their main contact center."

"Olivia, this is crazy! Can't you do something?" pleaded Lenore.

Whoa! They had never acted like this before. I had worked with these people for years and never seen them so angry and agitated. I had to get them to calm down and comply with HR's orders, or their worst fears would be realized.

Luckily I didn't follow my initial, knee-jerk reaction, which was to get angry at them for whining to me about something I could do nothing about.

As their leader I did not have the luxury of venting and complaining. I stopped myself in time to take stock of the situation: these were understandably upset, frightened people voicing their concerns. As I applied SODA, I accomplished the first three steps, *Stop*, *Observe* the situation for what it was, and *Decide* how I wanted to respond. But I wasn't so sure I could *Act* in a way that would persuade them to let go of their fear and thinking the worst.

Gathering my courage, I eased into a chair at the head of the table, sat up straight, and took a deep breath. I placed Izzy on my lap out of sight. Using my softest, calmest voice, I said, "Okay, everyone. Let's all calm down so we can discuss this. Listen, I understand how you feel and how anxious you must be right now."

"Ya, right. Sure you do," someone whispered sarcastically. I let that pass.

"Since the merger was announced three months ago you've seen the teams of auditors from Imperator Energy visiting various departments. They are taking a close look at how we operate as a company and examining our financial performance.

The interviews HR is asking us to do are part of that pre-merger examination process."

"Correction, boss," said Nikki. "We aren't being *asked* to do these interviews—we don't have a choice. We have to do them!"

"Just so you know," I continued. "I did not see this coming. I'm as surprised as you are that we have to reapply for our current positions. I know it doesn't seem fair, that we should have to be interviewed for the same job we've been doing for years. I wish I had a magic wand to make this disappear. But I don't. The fact is HR wants us all to make appointments to be interviewed, so that's what we are going to do. My interview is scheduled for this afternoon."

Our most senior representative, Lorraine, asked the question on everyone's mind. "What if we refuse to have an interview? Do you think they'd really fire us? I can't believe they'd do that. In the old days this never would have happened!"

"Are you kidding?" replied Lanny. "Darlin,' you are going to have to get real. Of course, they'd fire us—in a heartbeat. They'd be happy if we flunked the interview. It just means they'll have fewer people to dispose of. I think this might be the end of the road for all of us."

"All right," I said lowering my voice to just above a whisper, "let's all take a deep breath, step back for a second so we can see our situation for what it is."

I noticed Milo was unusually quiet. His shoulders had sunk, as if he'd given up. I softened my gaze and looked at him as I would if he were one of my children who was hurting. He looked away, took a deep breath, and sighed.

"Obviously, we all want to continue working for Mighty Power. We are invested in this place. Many of us have built our professional careers here. I know I have. We do an amazing job. On those hectic Monday mornings when the volume of calls coming in is more than we can handle, and we have fifty calls in queue, we get through it by working together— as a team. We have always stuck together. I know we will get through this, too.

"As for me, I started here as a service rep and spent the last four years as your supervisor. I genuinely love what I do and want to keep doing it.

Truth be told, I'm probably more attached to my job than I should be.

"Those of you who have worked here awhile remember our good friend, Isabel. Since she retired a couple of years ago, we try to meet for coffee when we can. The other day I was telling Isabel how freaked out I was at the prospect of losing my job, that I couldn't imagine working anywhere else. I was hoping she would sympathize with my plight and say something to make me feel better. But true to form, she didn't tell me what I wanted to hear. Instead she reminded me of the wisdom story she told me back when I was just as worried and stressed about getting promoted to supervisor. I was so obsessed with getting that job I was making myself crazy with worry."

I told my team the same story Isabel told me about the greedy monkey that reached into a trap to grab an enticing treat. What the monkey didn't know was that the opening was only large enough for its hand to fit through. As long as it held on to the food it wanted so badly it would be caught in the trap. But if it relaxed its grip and let go of what

Aha! #30

Courage is being scared to death and doing it anyway.

it wanted, it could withdraw its hand and go free.

I brought Izzy up from my lap and positioned him on the table in front of me and asked, "Anybody see a parallel between the monkey's situation and ours?"

Milo suddenly looked up. He grabbed Izzy, held him high so everyone could see him, and declared, "Guys, I hate to say this, but we are all acting like helpless, hopeless, stuck monkeys. We are holding on to what we want for dear life. The more desperate we are to keep our jobs the more trapped we feel. We gotta let it go!"

I scanned the faces in the room to see if what Milo said registered. I was relieved to see it did.

Now it was time to address Nikki, our team's official naysayer. "Nikki," I said. "You said you don't have a choice—you're being forced to reapply for your job. Actually, that's not true. We all have a choice. If we decide we don't want to go through the reapplication process we're free to look for a position elsewhere. I know it's hard to imagine letting go of your job. But if we can deal with the possibility we may have to find another job, I'm quite sure we'll feel better about our situation. And a lot less stressed.

"As for me, I have to admit there are many days when I feel a lot like a stuck monkey. That's why I am so fond of that little monkey. Every time I look at that toy monkey I'm reminded of a lesson I keep trying to learn—that the more effort and energy I put into trying to control things that are way beyond my control, the more stressed I get. Right now I'm trying really hard to be okay with whatever happens with the merger. I'm not near as mellow about it as I'd like to be. But, I want you to know that I'm trying—trying to stay calm, be patient, and wait to see what happens.

"So I'd like you all to try to do that, too," I continued. "Try your best not to worry so much about what may or may not happen after the merger. Right now we still have our jobs. Let's just take one day at a time and wait to see what happens."

"Easy for you to say. You've got a husband to help pay the bills," complained Nikki.

"Nikki," I replied. "That's my whole point. Dealing with stuff like this isn't easy—for anybody.

There is no Easy Button we can push to make it all go away. We just have to accept that it is what it is.

"But really," I continued, "when you think about it, what choice do we have? Go around moping, being paranoid, and spinning worst-case scenarios? That gets us nowhere. Or do we make the decision to go about our business, make the best of the situation, and deal with whatever happens when it happens? That's a choice each of us have to make for ourselves."

Milo, still holding the monkey, gave him an affectionate squeeze and handed him back to me. "Any chance you have any more of these monkeys?" he grinned.

THE MONKEY, THE MOON & MAYBE

CHAPTER NINE: THE INTERVIEW

My interview would have gone a lot better had I taken my own advice. As I entered the elevator to go up to the executive offices on the fifth floor for my interview, I noticed how terribly nervous I was. I could feel the beads of sweat forming on my forehead. With each passing floor I felt more and more anxious. And tense. I wondered if this is what an anxiety attack felt like.

When I got off the elevator I walked past the executive offices and saw our CEO, Mr. Mathwig, sitting around a table engrossed in what looked like a serious discussion with a bunch of executive types— probably from Imperator Energy. I wondered if they had any idea how stressful it was for employees to have to wait for them to make a decision about the merger. We didn't know any more than we did three months ago.

By the time I arrived at the small windowless conference room, my heart was racing. I handed my paperwork to the interviewer and forced a smile. I had not seen the man before.

"Good morning. You must be Olivia. Please, have a seat. Give me a minute to review your file. So how is your day going so far?" he asked as he looked over the documents.

"Pretty well, I guess," I muttered, shifting in my chair, "if you consider that I have a team that would mutiny if they could and toss me overboard in the process."

The man looked up from the table. "Oh, that doesn't sound good. I don't suppose it has anything to do with having to reapply for their jobs," he replied, attempting a smile.

"No kidding," I replied. "It's pretty hard to put a positive spin on us all having to interview for the jobs we've been doing, and doing well, for years."

"That's entirely understandable. I know how hard it must be to have to deal with all the uncertainty," replied the interviewer. "Allow me to introduce myself. My name is Anthony Murphy. I work for a firm retained by Imperator Energy to conduct these employee assessments."

I had no idea that figuring out a way to fire employees who didn't fit the new corporate structure was a job somebody was paid to do.

My cheeks were burning hot. I was sweating bullets. My heart was pounding so fast it hurt. I tried to contain myself by crossing my arms and taking a deep breath. I sat back in my chair. It didn't help.

"Look, is this interview really necessary?" I snapped. "Whatever you need to know is all right there in my personnel file. When it comes to performance, I'm proud to say, my team has been one of the top teams the last couple of years."

"Except lately, I see," Mr. Murphy replied. "According to this latest report your team has slipped quite a bit in the rankings. In fact, last month your team came in last. What do you think is the reason for that?"

I couldn't believe he would even have to ask the question. The answer was so obvious.

"Well . . ." I replied, swallowing hard. "Let's start with being short staffed. We are down from our original twenty reps to only fifteen. We lost our five temps right after the merger was announced."

My voice ratcheted louder as I asked, "Do you think that just maybe the survivors are terrified, wondering when they will be laid off? My people are downright scared."

"So, Mr. Murphy," I sneered. "Do you think that might explain why my people aren't real motivated at the moment?"

"Maybe you can tell me," I continued, not waiting for a reply. "How the heck I am supposed to keep morale up and produce great results with a team of demoralized, paranoid people?"

I leaned across the table and glowered at him. "If you have a solution for my little morale problem, I'd love to hear it!" I barked.

Mr. Murphy appeared unfazed. He asked, "Is it possible that you're feeling the same way? That you are thinking you're going to be out of a job, too?"

How could he even ask the question?

I threw up my hands. "Well, what do *you* think?"

As I heard myself utter those angry words I realized how out of control I was. If there was ever a time I should have applied SODA, this was it. Feeling mortified and terribly ashamed of my behavior, it was all I could do to not stand up and bolt out the door.

I melted into my chair, hung my head, and took a long, deep breath. "I am *so* sorry." I winced. "As you can probably tell, I'm more than a little emotional about this. I can't tell you how sorry I am for losing it like that. That was incredibly unprofessional. I hope you'll accept my apology."

"That's all right, Olivia. Don't worry about it," replied the interviewer. "Having conducted hundreds of these interviews, believe me, I have seen plenty of people get upset and combative. Compared to the combat I saw when I was in the military these interviews are a piece of cake."

Suddenly I noticed he was sitting very upright— in a wheelchair. I hadn't noticed the wheelchair before. I felt even worse.

Aha! #31

**Barn's burnt down.
Now I can see the moon.**

"Where did you serve?" I tried not to stare.

"I was in Afghanistan. I did two tours of duty before I got shot. I had a spinal injury the doctors thought wouldn't be permanent. But after two surgeries and months of physical therapy the doctors at the VA broke the news: I would never walk again. I would have to use a wheelchair the rest of my life."

"Oh. I'm so sorry. I can't imagine how hard that must have been for you to accept."

"You know, it was. I was beyond angry at first. I refused to accept the doctor's verdict. I got a second opinion—and a third. But all the experts told me the same thing: I would never walk again.

"Honestly? I was so mad I took it out on everybody around me. I was impossible to live with. I acted like a real jerk. I did an about-face when one of the therapists I'd been working with, who probably got fed up with my 'poor me' routine, suddenly stopped and pointed to a poster on the wall.

"I will never forget that poster as long as I live. It showed a smoldering pile of rubble, what was probably a large barn that had burned to the ground. The ashes of that barn were bathed in the white light cast by a big, bright, luminous moon. At the bottom, the poster read, 'Barn's burnt down. Now I can see the moon.'

"Those words and that image really hit me," he continued. "Up until that moment I was so busy mourning what I'd lost, staring at the ashes, I never thought to look up to see that big, beautiful moon. Once I did, I could see that a future was possible. I was able to move on. I can't say it was easy at first. Far from it. Aside from using this wheel chair to get around, I live a pretty normal life. I have a good job, a wife, a couple of kids and a house in the suburbs. I thank God every single day for being alive."

I assumed I already flunked the interview, but I did the best I could to answer the rest of Mr. Murphy's questions. After it was over I walked out of the room feeling defeated. Not only had I been incredibly rude to a guy just trying to do his job—a man who'd been through more pain and suffering than I ever would—I just bungled whatever chance I had to keep the best job I ever had.

CHAPTER TEN: WOULDA SHOULDA COULDA

On the drive into work the next morning, I replayed the interview in my mind for the hundredth time. I thought about the various points in the conversation when I could have stopped myself from getting so upset. When I should have just shut up.

When I arrived at my office, I hung up my coat. I picked up Izzy from my desk, plopped down in my chair, and looked him in the eye. "Well, my furry friend, I believe you are looking at one soon-to-be-unemployed supervisor. I don't know what came over me to act that way. I guess all the frustration and anger I've been feeling came out all at once. I should have known better than to let my emotions take over."

I called Isabel to fill her in on what had happened. I cringed as I gave my friend a blow-by-blow report of my conversation with the interviewer —and my angry outburst.

"As you pointed out," Isabel replied, "the interview would have gone much better had you maintained your composure. I'm sure you will do better next time."

I shook my head. "I seriously doubt if there will be a next time. I shouldn't have acted that way. I think whatever career I had at Mighty Power is officially over."

"Olivia, please stop 'shoulding' on yourself. It's not healthy," Isabel replied.

"Excuse me?" I said.

"You just said you behaved in a way you 'shouldn't' have. That was an act of 'shoulding.' Not helpful. Not useful."

I had no idea where she was going with this. Was "shoulding" a real word?

"What you may not realize, my dear," Isabel continued, "is that whenever you are talking to yourself and you use the word 'should,' consider it a red flag, a warning that you are entering dangerous territory. Take for example, the situation with the interviewer yesterday. You said some things you now regret. You told me, quote: 'I shouldn't have acted that way.' Olivia, that's a perfect example of shoulding."

"Okay, I admit I 'should' on myself, as you put it," I replied. "But that's just my self-talk; it's not hurting anybody. I'm just trying to make sense of what happened."

"Olivia, that's not true! When are you going to understand that much of your misery is self-inflicted? You are your own worst enemy. Every time you ridicule yourself because things didn't turn out the way you expected, your self-esteem takes a hit.

"Shoulding starts with your own belief that things *should* be a certain way. Going into that interview you had high expectations. You expected to impress the interviewer with your qualifications. But you fell short of your expectations. You regret losing your temper. Now you feel guilty and are beating yourself up for it."

"So," I replied, "what you are telling me is that having high expectations gets me into trouble. Are you suggesting it's better to go through life always expecting the worst? If I have low expectations I can save myself from ever being disappointed."

"Olivia, that is not what I said," she replied softly. "Going through life expecting the worst would be a horrible way to live. But thinking life should always be neat and tidy and free of disappointment is not realistic either. Why not take the middle way? Realize that stuff happens—that life will be messy at times."

"I guess I am beginning to get that, given the fact that my life isn't exactly working out as planned," I said ruefully.

"You know," I continued, "that reminds me of the guy who interviewed me yesterday. Talk about somebody being disappointed." I told Isabel how angry the man was when he found out he'd be permanently disabled. He realized a future was possible when he read the words, "Barn's burnt down. Now I can see the moon."

"Ah, that's a beautiful saying," said Isabel. "It's an old Japanese haiku I think."

"Olivia," she continued, "you should go back and thank that man. He gave you a tremendous gift. The story he told you of how he bounced back from adversity and the haiku were lessons in resiliency. When you think about it, everybody experiences setbacks. Some are minor disappointments that we get over quickly. But the more serious events, like losing a loved one, getting seriously ill, or, in the case of the interviewer, being injured and permanently disabled, can alter the course of a person's life forever.

"Fortunately, with the passage of time, most people are like that man. They face reality—their life will never be the same as it was and they need to adjust to their new circumstances. Many people, the resilient ones, are surprised to discover that living through that wrenching experience has enriched their lives in ways they never imagined possible. Olivia, cultivating the ability to be resilient, being able to face adversity head on, is crucial if you want to be truly happy. Resiliency gives us the strength we need to bounce back stronger, wiser, and feeling personally more powerful."

"I believe I had one of those experiences!" I said eagerly. "When Jake and I got married, we wanted to start a family right away. After a few months I got pregnant. We were so happy! We decorated the nursery and got ready to welcome our new baby into our lives. But in the third month I had a miscarriage. Jake and I were devastated. But we didn't want to give up on our dream of being parents, so we tried again. That pregnancy lasted two months. The third pregnancy lasted only a few weeks.

"Fortunately Jake and I didn't give up. With the help of a fertility clinic I got pregnant a fourth time. Nine months later we were blessed with our twins, Nate and Natalie."

"I'm so sorry that happened, Olivia," replied Isabel. "I can't imagine what it would have been like to be a young couple so thrilled at the prospect of a new baby only to be disappointed not once, but three times. So, you could say that was your equivalent to the barn burning down. Had you and Jake not been so resilient, you wouldn't have those twins of yours. Being blessed with your twins was your 'moon.'"

I glanced at my computer and saw the pop-up reminder letting me know my team meeting was in ten minutes. "Oh, Isabel, talking with you is always so good for me, but I have to go. I need to get to a meeting with my team. Wish me luck! I'll check in with you later." My wise friend had given me an idea.

As I walked to the conference room, I reviewed the agenda for the meeting in my mind. Besides the usual topics—a review of the latest performance results and recent policy changes we needed to implement—I had to allow enough time for my team to talk about how we were going to get through the next few weeks or months in one piece.

I looked around the table at the anxious faces of my team. They looked so sad and discouraged. I had hoped yesterday's pep talk would boost their spirits. But I could see they were back in the doldrums.

Aha! #32

The real disaster is the loss of hope.

My team had changed. Prior to the merger announcement, they were a tight-knit group. When things got tough, they rallied and got through it together. They genuinely cared about each other. But, not any more. Now they looked at the service rep in the next cubical as a rival competing for whatever jobs might be left after the merger. I was spending more of my time settling petty arguments and trying to keep the peace.

This team was beginning to look a lot like the team I inherited when I filled in as a temporary team leader early in my career. That team was beyond dysfunctional. Those people genuinely hated each other. When I took over as team leader, I tried everything I could think of to get them to stop their bickering. Nothing worked. Finally I went to Isabel for help. As usual, instead of telling me what to do, she told me another of her wisdom stories and let me figure out the lesson it had to offer.

I gathered that motley crew of discontents together in a circle and told them Isabel's story of the Fighting Melons. [See Page 126.] They recognized themselves. They were acting a lot like the melons in the story. Their constant arguing and fighting was getting them nowhere. They understood that the only way they could succeed was to put aside their differences and start working together. That story— along with a lot of generosity and hard work— transformed them into a happier, more unified team.

I wasn't at all sure whether it was possible to leverage the power of a story a second time. But I decided I had to try.

CHAPTER ELEVEN: A MOON IN THEIR POCKET

After we took care of the business portion of the meeting, I asked my team to push the conference room table to the side and arrange their chairs in a circle. There was shuffling and muttering as they took their seats. I could tell they were wondering why the new seating arrangement.

I started with Nikki. "Nikki, you are the only one here who was on my team when I was a team leader. So, maybe you can guess why we are sitting in a circle."

She smiled and nodded. "I do remember that meeting. Our team was in really bad shape at the time. We were constantly squabbling and sniping at each other. After you told us the story of the Fighting Melons, we stopped being so selfish and got our groove back. In fact, we ended up being the best-performing team in the call center. Boss, I can't imagine you doing the same thing with this team, if that's what you're thinking. We are about as depressed as fifteen people can be."

"I can see that," I replied. "Living with all this uncertainty, not knowing what's going to happen with the merger—it's incredibly stressful."

"So what I'd like to do today," I continued, "is share an Aha! moment I had recently. I want to tell you about it because I think it will help you look at the change we are going through in a different way." I paused for a second, smiled, and said, "It's about finding your moon."

My team looked at me as if they hadn't heard me right.

"That's right. I said 'moon.'"

I told the group the story the interviewer told me about how angry he was when he found out he would never walk again and the haiku that saved him. "The man said that the message on that poster is what got him to let go of his fear of the future and see his situation in a new light. It gave him hope. The poster read, 'Barn's burnt down. Now I can see the moon.'"

To my surprise, everyone in the circle nodded and smiled. The interviewer must have told them the same story.

Lenore said, "When I left the interview, I felt a little better about my situation. I think everybody else did too. If that man can survive getting shot and disabled fighting a war," she smiled, "I don't see why we can't get through a little thing like a merger." The others nodded in agreement.

"You know," I replied, "I have to admit I went into the interview feeling pretty angry—insulted, really—to have to go through an interview. But I think what bothered me most was feeling so helpless, that I had no control over what was going to happen to me. That my career, my future, depended on what management decides to do.

"That man's story and that beautiful haiku

helped me see that even if the worse did happen, if I ended up losing my job, I would live through it. I'd eventually find another job. Who knows? Maybe I'd land a job I liked even better. It made me realize that when disaster hits we have a choice. We can do what he did at first—stay stuck in the past, feel helpless—like a victim. Or we can choose to take control of our lives. Make the decision to move on, to look up from the ashes of what used to be and see the possibilities of a future, to see the 'moon.'"

I told my team my personal story, how I discovered my moon. About how devastated Jake and I were when I had one miscarriage after another.

"Each time I lost a baby I thought I couldn't go on. I wanted to give up. Thank goodness, Jake had enough faith for both of us. He convinced me it was only a matter of time before we became parents. I'm so glad we didn't give up. I was blessed with two moons, my son and daughter, Nate and Natalie." I looked around the room. "Does anyone else know what I'm talking about?"

Lanny spoke first. "My dad managed the meter readers for Mighty Power. He had worked for the company for thirty years and made a good living. He liked the company a lot and wanted me to build a career here, too. So when I dropped out of college after a couple of years and didn't know what I wanted to do, I decided to join the company. When I got my job as a meter reader, my dad was so happy and proud of me.

"Everything was great until about five years ago. My dad had a massive heart attack and died the same day. Shortly after that I found out the company was bringing on new technology that made my job as a meter reader obsolete. But instead of being laid off, I was offered the option to work as a service representative in the call center. I hated the idea of being stuck behind a desk all day, but I decided to give it a try anyway. I was surprised to find out I had a knack for working with customers. My moon was finding a job that is perfect for me."

Several nodded when they realized they had a similar story to tell. As we went around the circle each person shared a personal story of a time when she or he had transformed adversity into a blessing.

Lenore told us about her husband leaving her

Aha! #33

The most important thing
is to remember
the most important thing.

with two young children to support. She struggled for years as a single parent, barely getting by. When she met and married Tom, her life changed for the better. Her moon was finding the love of her life.

Nikki shared her story of having breast cancer ten years ago. That experience made her realize that every day was a gift. She said she completed the chemo treatment and is now free of cancer. Her moon was getting her health back.

Lorraine told us that back in the seventies when she gave birth to a daughter who had Down syndrome she and her husband had to make a decision. At the time, many parents in their situation put their babies in institutions. "My husband and I decided to keep our baby girl," Lorraine said. "Our Betsy has brought so much joy into our lives, I can't imagine life without her. My daughter is my moon."

We ended our meeting with Milo's story of devastation. "When I was young, my family lived in Oklahoma," he said. "Back then there were no reliable tornado warnings, so we had no idea our house was directly in the path of one of the worst tornadoes they ever had. My mom, my two brothers, and I huddled together in the bathtub and survived. But not my dad. He was driving home, trying to get to us, and was swept up by the tornado. Pieces of his truck were found a few miles away, but they never found his body. Of course, the tornado wiped out everything we owned. We had to start all over again but without my dad. That was the worst part. It took a few years and a lot of hard work by my mom, my brothers, and me, but we got back on our feet. That experience, as tough as it was, ended up bringing my brothers and me a lot closer. Those guys are still my best friends. So I'd say my brothers Gabe and Theo are my moons."

As they filed out of the conference room to go back to work, each member of my team had a precious moon tucked in his or her pocket.

CHAPTER TWELVE:
MAYBE. MAYBE NOT. WE'LL SEE.

Three weeks later Mighty Power's CEO called a second all-employee meeting. I hoped this was the day we would finally learn our fate.

Mr. Mathwig looked very tired, like he hadn't had much sleep. He began the meeting by thanking the employees. "I know you are all anxious to find out where we are with the merger," he said.

"The last four months haven't been easy—for any of us. I appreciate you all being so patient. I understand how difficult it was to have to go through those interviews. Thanks, too, for cooperating with the team of auditors that performed the pre-merger assessment."

"The reason I called this meeting is to inform you of our decision. I wanted to tell you in person. Last night there was a joint meeting of our board of directors and Imperator Energy's board. Now that the final report is in we had to decide if we move forward with the merger."

Mr. Mathwig paused and looked out at the sea of eight hundred anxious faces. "I have good news to report," he grinned. "Both boards agreed *not* to proceed any further. Mighty Power will *not* be merging with Imperator Energy. As of today, the merger is officially *off*."

Finally, a decision had been made! A collective gasp rose from the crowd. Everyone stood up at once. The sound of the cheers and applause echoed throughout the building. Once the applause died down, Mr. Mathwig told us that over the next few months he and the members of the board were going to consider their options. He didn't foresee any significant changes in the short term.

"Like many of you, I am very proud to work for Mighty Power," he said. "It's a great company that has served this region for the last forty-eight years. Believe me, I would like nothing more than to see us continue to operate independently. Honestly, I don't know whether that's possible. But one thing I can tell you is that the board of directors and I are committed to doing everything we can to keep Mighty Power intact."

As the crowd filed out of the room, there was lots of excited chatter. We were all relieved to learn we still had jobs. Well, almost all. Luis was walking beside me lost in thought. I wondered whether he would go ahead with his plan to leave the company and work for his father-in-law.

"Are you disappointed?" I asked.

"I have to admit that I am," sighed Luis. "I sure didn't expect this. We were counting on the severance package to help make the transition easier. Now I don't know what we will do. I'll have to wait to see what management ultimately decides to do. I guess for the time being I'm not going anywhere." I gave him a quick hug.

That evening I told Jake the good news, that I would be keeping my job after all. He was probably thinking, "I told you so." I was glad he didn't rub it in. No doubt he was relieved to have his wife back.

It took a few days for my team to settle in to what had become the new normal, getting more done with fewer people. They had returned to happily working together. Even negative Nikki arrived at work each morning in a good mood.

The following Saturday after dropping Nate off at soccer practice I met Isabel for coffee. I wanted to tell her my good news in person. When I sat down, I removed Izzy from my purse and set him on the table.

"I see you brought along your monkey pal. It's good to see him again." She picked Izzy up and looked him over. "You know, I forgot how cute he is. He hasn't aged a bit."

"I want to thank you again for giving him to me," I replied. "Having him to talk to really helped me get through some of my toughest days. Sometimes all a person really needs is somebody to just listen to them; somebody to tell their troubles to. Izzy is an excellent listener."

When I told Isabel that management called off the merger, she didn't look at all surprised.

"So, after all that, it ended up to be much ado about nothing," she said, grinning.

"Well, I don't think I'd call it 'nothing,'" I replied, feeling a bit defensive. "The merger was something that could have happened. I'm just relieved it didn't."

"But really, thinking back over the last several months, was it worth all the agony you put yourself through?" asked Isabel.

I laughed ruefully. As usual, my friend was right. I could have saved myself the trouble.

"Olivia," Isabel continued, "I had some surprising news yesterday. I've not had much energy lately, feeling a bit rundown, so I decided to see my doctor. She ran some tests and came back with a preliminary diagnosis of leukemia."

I didn't know what to say. The thought of Isabel getting sick never occurred to me.

"Isn't that a type of cancer?" I asked.

"Yes, it is. I'll find out what type of leukemia I

have after I see the specialist on Monday."

"Oh, Isabel. That's terrible! You of all people!"

Isabel reached across the table to comfort me. Taking my hand in hers, she said, "Olivia, I know it's upsetting to think about. Nobody wants to hear they have cancer. My doctor told me that if it turns out to be one of the more common forms of leukemia, it's very treatable. I'm just taking one day at a time. Right now I'm in 'maybe mode.'"

"'Maybe mode'?" I asked.

"Let me explain," she continued. "Last night as I was thinking about this I was reminded of a parable my mother told me when I was going through my divorce. I was unnerved by all the changes that were coming at me all at once. That story reminded me that no event, in and of itself, should be viewed as good or bad, lucky or unlucky, but that only time will tell. It's best to say to yourself, 'It will be interesting to see what happens.' This is the story my mother told me:

> Once upon a time there was an old farmer. One day his horse ran away. When his neighbors heard of his misfortune, they

sympathized and said, 'Such bad luck.'

'Maybe. Maybe not. We will see,' replied the farmer.

The following day the horse returned accompanied by three wild horses. 'How wonderful!' the neighbors exclaimed.

'Maybe. Maybe not. We will see,' replied the old man.

The next day his only son attempted to ride one of the wild horses, was thrown off, and broke his leg. Again his neighbors offered their sympathy for his misfortune.

'Maybe. Maybe not. We will see,' said the old man, shrugging.

The next day soldiers rode into the village looking for young men to draft into the army. When they saw the son's broken leg they passed him by. The neighbors were overjoyed that the old farmer's misfortune had turned out to be a blessing.

'Maybe. Maybe not. We will see,' the farmer replied.

Aha! #34

Right now. Right here.
I'm okay.

Upon hearing Isabel's story, I felt envious of that wise old farmer—and of her. The farmer dealt with his changing circumstances, both good and bad, by resting in "maybe," by choosing the middle way. Now Isabel was doing the same thing with her cancer diagnosis. She was taking a wait and see approach. Had I done that, had I stopped long enough to see the loss of my job as only a possibility, to have been patient, to wait to see what happened, I could have avoided all the stress and drama I put myself through. Drama, I now realize, that was created by me.

I gave Isabel a hug and said good-bye. I promised to call her on Tuesday to find out what the specialist had to say. As I got ready to leave, I gave Izzy a squeeze and returned him to my bag. My monkey friend would have a special place on my desk from now on—a daily reminder not to be overly attached to outcomes.

When I picked up my coffee cup, I was surprised to discover that the napkin sitting under the cup had coffee stains on it in the shape of two circles, complete with a space in the middle. This was the same image Isabel drew on a napkin and gave to me when I was a new service rep! I slipped the napkin into my purse for safekeeping in hopes that the next time life throws me a curve I will remember to take the middle way.

Seeing another napkin on the table, I took out a pen and wrote the words I plan to live by from now on: "Right now. Right here. I'm okay."

THE END

12 AHA!S FOR LIVING LIFE FEARLESSLY

Aha! #23: Life is full of surprises. Expect the unexpected.

Aha! #24: It's not enough to be sorry. Sometimes you actually have to change.

Aha! #25: No matter where you go there you are.

Aha! #26: Life is messy. (It's supposed to be.)

Aha! #27: React or respond. You decide.

Aha! #28: We all have inner wisdom. A true friend helps us find it.

Aha! #29: Sometimes learning is remembering what you already know.

Aha! #30: Courage is being scared to death and doing it anyway.

Aha! #31: Barn's burnt down. Now I can see the moon.

Aha! #32: The real disaster is the loss of hope.

Aha! #33: The most important thing is to remember the most important thing.

Aha! #34: Right now. Right here. I'm okay.

OLIVIA'S 22 AHA!S FROM
THE NAPKIN, THE MELON & THE MONKEY
BY BARBARA BURKE

Aha! #1:   I will always have problems.

Aha! #2:   It's not about me.

Aha! #3:   Problems can be gifts in disguise.

Aha! #4:   Just sit there. Do nothing.

Aha! #5:   There is no such thing as a difficult situation.

Aha! #6:   When all else fails, have a SODA.

Aha! #7:   Withholding judgment allows me to observe what is.

Aha! #8:   The nicer I am to myself, the nicer I am to others.

Aha! #9:   A simple apology works wonders.

Aha! #10:   The less I talk, the more I learn.

Aha! #11:   People harmonize when they are tuned to the same frequency.

Aha! #12:   Great supervisors follow the Golden Rule and do the right thing.

Aha! #13:   Spreading my wings is the only way
to fly.

Aha! #14:   Give a little. Get a lot.

Aha! #15:   Remember, we all share the same vine.

Aha! #16:   United we stand. Divided we fall.

Aha! #17:   Our stories connect us with each other.

Aha! #18:   Success comes from bringing out the
best in others.

Aha! #19:   Winners don't just point out problems.
They fix them.

Aha! #20:   It's not what happens to you in life, it's
what you do with what happens that
counts.

Aha! #21:   Real freedom comes from letting go of
the outcome.

Aha! #22:   Generous hearts make a difference.

THE STORY OF THE FIGHTING MELONS

Once upon a time there was a farmer who was known for miles around for raising the largest and sweetest watermelons. One year, his garden was blessed with abundant rainfall and plenty of sunshine. As his melons grew larger and larger—becoming the biggest ones ever—he heard disturbing noises coming from his melon patch. The melons were fighting!

The farmer dropped his hoe and hurried to the patch. "What is the trouble?" he exclaimed. A riot ensued. All the watermelons were yelling, screaming, and blaming each other. The noise was deafening.

He looked over his melon patch with new eyes. He could see the problem. Ideal growing conditions had produced melons of unusually large size. The result? The melons were so huge they were bumping up against each other.

The farmer wondered, "What can I do? How can I restore peace to my melon patch?" He thought and thought until he came upon a solution.

After several attempts to quiet the melons so he could speak, he finally got them to stop screaming. He had their full attention.

"Oh, my beautiful melons, I am so sorry for your troubles. But I am afraid that I am not the one to settle your arguments."

This time the outcry was even louder.

"But I know of something you can do to end your conflict. I guarantee that if each of you follows my instructions, you will live in harmony forever."

With that, the melons became very quiet. They were ready to hear what they could do to end their suffering.

"I'd like you to feel what you have at the top of your body," he instructed. The melons did as the farmer asked and looked at him, expecting something more than the obvious. Of course, there was a vine sticking out on top.

"Now, my dear melons, I'd like you to follow

that vine to its end." The melons obeyed and traced the vine, past the many leaves. "Keep going," the farmer encouraged. "Keep going until you find the end of your vine."

All of a sudden there was dead silence. A soft, collective sigh rose from the patch. The melons had discovered that they were all one plant.

From that day forward, the melons lived in peace and harmony. They grew to record size and won many awards at the county fair that year. Everyone agreed that the farmer's melons were the biggest and the sweetest.

ACKNOWLEDGMENTS

First I'd like to thank the fans of my first book, *The Napkin, the Melon & the Monkey* for giving me the idea to write a sequel. At book signings and in my seminars, readers who felt a strong connection with Olivia, the main character in the story, asked me what happened to her. I'd assure them she was doing fine, still working at Mighty Power, enjoying her new job as a supervisor. "Thanks for asking," I'd politely reply.

In truth, I had no idea how Olivia was. I hadn't talked to her in ages. I decided to find out.

This book catches up with Olivia four years after the end of *The Napkin, the Melon & the Monkey* and chronicles her emotional reaction to a series of events that could change her life forever. The lessons Olivia learns about resiliency and the 12 Aha!s she discovers on her journey provide the road map she needs to live with uncertainty at work and in life.

I hope you enjoy following Olivia's most recent transformation and find the lessons she learned useful the next time life throws you a curve you didn't expect—or want. I encourage you to share Olivia's story with your co-workers, friends and family.

In addition to the people who inspired me to write the book, I want to thank the individuals who helped me craft the story and produce the book. A big thanks goes to my sister Susan Fotos and my daughter Megan Fluegel for reading the first versions of the book. You delivered the encouragement I needed when I needed it and offered many suggestions and ideas that made the story stronger.

I appreciate the generosity of Gail Jones Hansen, Susie DeMalignon, Nancy Brown, Laura Schenck, Michael Carroll, Deb Nagurski, Ed Kolodziej, Joan Holman, and Tim Johnston, who read the manuscript and let me know I was on the right track.

I doubt if this book would have made it into print without the able assistance of my production team—all of whom live in Northfield Minnesota the small college town where I live. A big thanks to Carla Brown, the wildly talented artist who designed the book's cover, and to April Ripka for creating the image of the monkey to look exactly like Izzy, the

THE MONKEY, THE MOON & MAYBE

toy monkey character in the book. Thanks to my brother, photographer Tom Roster, for making me look better than I really do. I am grateful to Rikki Peterson for helping with both books. Not only did you edit the book midway through, your suggestions made the characters come to life. I also want to thank Nancy Ashmore, my very patient and caring editor. You've created another book I am very proud of.

I owe the biggest thanks to the people I rely on for support and guidance. Thank you, Mark Nunberg and Michael Carroll for sharing the teachings with me as I stumble toward enlightenment. Thanks to Deb Nagurski for helping me stay calm and carry on. And lastly, I want to thank my teacher Jazz who reminds me every day to be present for my life—and for being the best dog there ever was.

ABOUT THE AUTHOR

Barbara Burke is an internationally known consultant, speaker, and author specializing in the "people side" of customer service management. She is passionate about helping organizations generate long-term success by creating work environments in which employees feel valued and engaged. Barbara believes that when employees and their leaders rely on the basic core values of respect, kindness, compassion, and generosity to guide their interactions with each other and their customers, everyone benefits.

Over the last 28 years Barbara has worked with many top companies including: Honeywell, Microsoft, Time-Warner, Target, American Family Insurance, San Diego Gas & Electric, Progress Energy, Estée Lauder, Proctor & Gamble, Verizon, Cox Communications, Alltel, Aqua America, the State of Minnesota, and the State of Pennsylvania.

Barbara helps her clients achieve long-term success in three ways.

Leadership Training.

Barbara's popular leadership training program, Intentional Coaching, teaches front-line leaders coaching protocols that provide agents with the help and support they need to give customers the best possible service experience. Her popular hands-on workshops are customized to fit the needs of individual client companies. She also offers public workshops throughout the U.S. several times a year.

Consulting.

Barbara partners with her contact center clients to improve customer satisfaction, increase efficiency, and build front-line engagement. She applies her proven culture change process to move the operation beyond efficient transaction handling to focusing on improving the quality of the customer experience.

Speaking.

As a thought leader on utilizing the customer service contact center as a strategic asset, Barbara is a popular presenter and keynote speaker at industry conferences. She provides inspiring seminars for corporate events and leadership retreats.

BRING BARBARA BURKE TO YOUR ORGANIZATION!

 Barbara's inspiring keynotes and seminars cover the topics of customer service, mindfulness, leadership, stress reduction, and managing change. Drawing on 28 years of experience, Barbara shares the many lessons she's learned about how to thrive (not just survive) amidst constant change. Her presentations are jam-packed with wisdom borne of practical know-how, light humor, and unforgettable, inspirational stories.

To schedule a speaking engagement, visit www.BarbaraBurke.com/speaking or email bb@BarbaraBurke.com.

Stay in touch with Barbara by subscribing to her free e-newsletter at www.BarbaraBurke.com/subscribe.

Each Monday Aha! offers sage advice and wisdom for leaders based on the Aha!s from her books.

START LIVING FEARLESSLY TODAY!

the
MONKEY
the MOON
& MAYBE

To learn more about products and services available to individuals and organizations, based on *The Monkey, the Moon & Maybe* visit www.MonkeyMoonMaybe.com, call (507) 663-7232 or email bb@BarbaraBurke.com.

Visit the book's website to buy the book and the e-book and learn how organizations can purchase quantities of books at a reduced price.

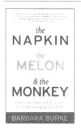

To learn more about products and services based on Barbara's customer service fable, *The Napkin, the Melon & the Monkey*, visit www.NapkinMelonMonkey.com.